This book belongs to:

....

AUTUMN
PUBLISHING

Published in 2021
First published in the UK by Autumn Publishing
An imprint of Igloo Books Ltd
Cottage Farm, NN6 0BJ, UK
Owned by Bonnier Books
Sveavägen 56, Stockholm, Sweden
www.autumnpublishing.co.uk

0721 001
2 4 6 8 10 9 7 5 3 1
ISBN 978-1-80108-183-2

Illustrated by Gisela Bohórquez
Written by Suzanne Fossey

Designed by Lee Italiano
Edited by Suzanne Fossey

Printed and manufactured in China

Little
CATERPiLLAR

 AUTUMN
PUBLISHING

I started as a little **egg**, small and **smooth** and round,

My **mummy** laid me on a plant, where I was **safe** and sound.

Safe inside my eggshell, I grew **bigger** all the time,

Until I got **so big**, I had
to **leave** my egg behind.

I wanted to **explore**, but I could **hear** a **bluebird's** song.
I thought it might be **hungry**, so I **hid** till it was **gone**.

I met some caterpillar friends – they looked a lot like me.

They were **munching** on the flowers,
and soon I felt... **hungry!**

I found a patch of flowers that were pretty, round and white.

My tum began to **rumble** so I took a great **big bite!**

I munched on leaves for two whole weeks, till I was fat and round.

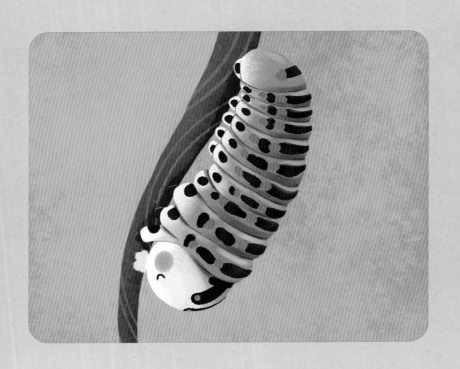

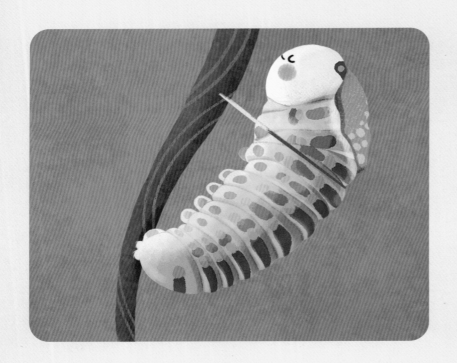

I spun a bed of silky thread, hidden out of sight.

Then I started to feel sleepy. It was time to snuggle down.

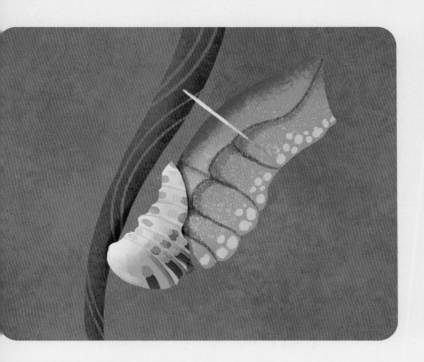
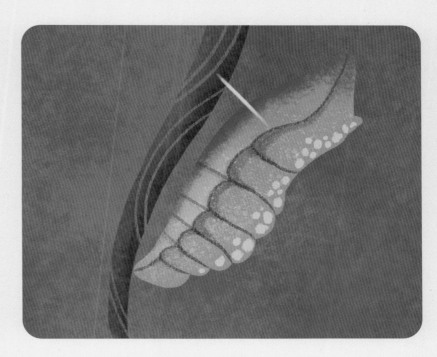

Then I turned into a chrysalis, and curled up for the night.

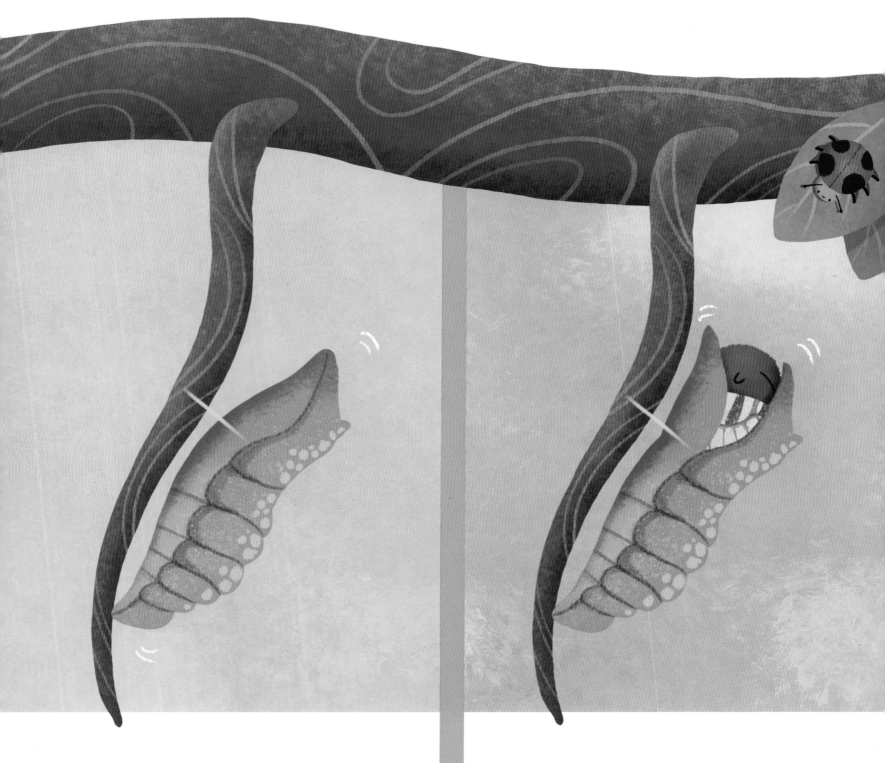

I snoozed inside my **chrysalis,** dreaming of the skies.

Inside me, things were **changing.** I woke to a **surprise!**

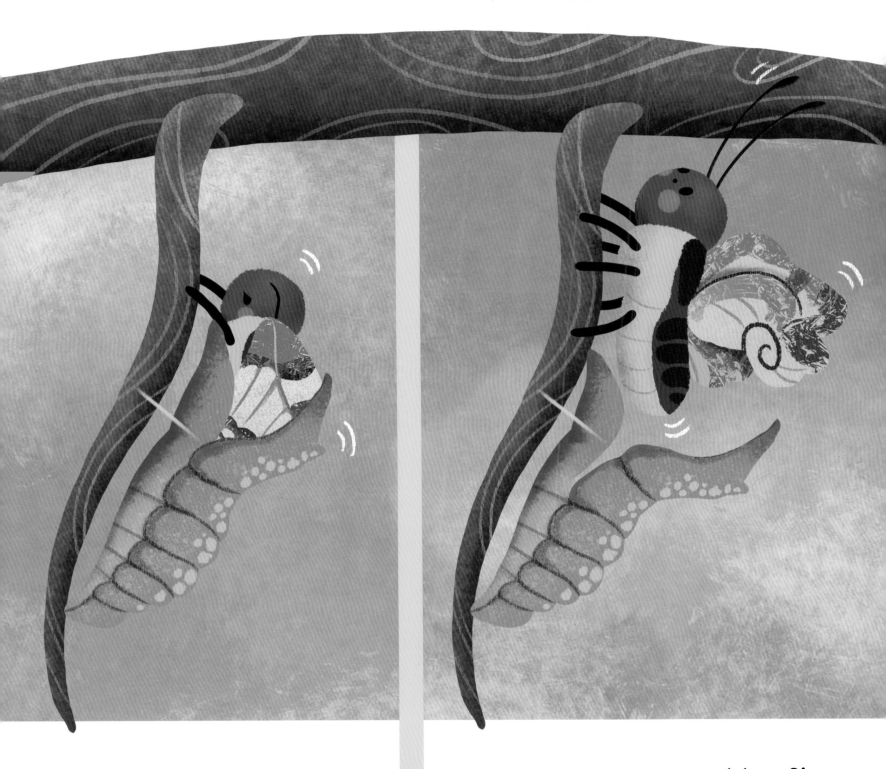

I pushed my way into the light,
and found that, of all things,

I'd turned into a **butterfly**,
with **crinkly** little **wings**!

I saw some other butterflies...

...swooping through the air.

Their pretty wings were spread out wide.

It really wasn't fair!

My poor wings were crumpled, quite damp and just too soft.
I had to wait for ages while they stretched out and dried off.

I stretched my wings and swooped down low...

... and flew through all the flowers.

It all felt so **amazing!**
I could **fly** around for **hours.**

I met another butterfly,
with wings as dashing as his smile.

He made me laugh
so he and I flew together for a while.

The summer came and went. Time had really flown!
Soon it was time for me to lay an egg all of my own.

I found a cosy spot upon a flower near a river,
and waited for my egg to become a little...

...caterpillar!

Caterpillars hatch out of tiny eggs, which are laid on plants. After they hatch, they spend all their time eating leaves, growing bigger and bigger. They often shed their skins and change colour as they grow. When they are big enough, caterpillars find a safe spot and shed their skins one last time, turning into a pupa or chrysalis. Inside the chrysalis, the caterpillar transforms into a butterfly. This change is called metamorphosis. The butterfly crawls out and stretches its wings, which are soft and crinkly at first. When its wings are dry, it can fly! The grown-up butterfly looks for a safe place to lay its own eggs, which will hatch into new caterpillars.